A Tune A Day

for Saxophone.

by C. Paul Herfurth.

Book Two.

Exclusive Distributors:
Music Sales Limited
8/9 Frith Street, London W1V 5TZ, England.
Music Sales Pty Limited
120 Rothschild Avenue, Rosebery, NSW 2018, Australia.

Order No. BM10231
ISBN 0.7119.1576.8

Boston Music Company.

PUPIL'S DAILY PRACTICE RECORD

Pupil fills in number of minutes of daily practice.

Parent signs initials in space designated as certification of pupil's record for the week.

Teacher fills in grade for quality of each week's work as shown by the lesson. Teacher signs initials.

E – Excellent; G – Good; M – Medium, L – Low

FIRST SEMESTER										SECOND SEMESTER									
Week	Mon.	Tues.	Wed.	Thur.	Fri.	Sat.	Parent's Initials	Weekly Grade	Teacher's Initials	Week	Mon.	Tues.	Wed.	Thur.	Fri.	Sat.	Parent's Initials	Weekly Grade	Teacher's Initials
1										1									
2										2									
3										3									
4										4									
5										5									

1st TEST GRADE			5th TEST GRADE		

6										6									
7										7									
8										8									
9										9									
10										10									

2nd TEST GRADE			6th TEST GRADE		

11										11									
12										12									
13										13									
14										14									
15										15									

3rd TEST GRADE			7th TEST GRADE		

16										16									
17										17									
18										18									
19										19									
20										20									

4th TEST GRADE			FINAL GRADE		

_____
Name

_____
Address

_____
School

_____
Grade

FOREWORD TO TEACHERS

"A TUNE A DAY" — Book Two for Saxophone represents a continuation of the philosophy and pedagogical principles set forth in Book One. Progress is approached through music rather than through technical exercises. However, routines for practice of technique during the lesson and at home are included, and the author intends that some pure technique be included with each lesson assignment, the amount being left to the discretion of the teacher.

Each of the twenty-seven "LESSON" assignments includes problems preparatory to the wide variety of good music that has been chosen to illustrate and give practice in the various skills to be learned. The author has selected material of composers which students will encounter in school bands and orchestras.

As ensemble playing is an invaluable aid to the teaching of musicianship, many duets, trios, and quartets have been included.

The material in this book enables the student to study the keys and scales to three sharps and three flats, the chromatic scale, and most rhythm problems encountered in school bands and orchestras.

It is my hope that this book will be instrumental in helping the student refine the many processes learned in Book One and help him gain greater fluency in reading and playing to develop into a young musician, not a "note player"

C. PAUL HERFURTH

TO THE STUDENT

Remember these important technics for wind instrument players.

(a) Developing and strengthening the lip muscles. (Process) Playing of long sustained tones every day.

(b) Developing clarity and precision in attacks. (Process) Proper use of the tongue.

(c) Developing a fine quality of tone. (Process) A combination of (a) and careful listening.

(d) Developing fluency in execution. (Process) Playing of scales and arpeggios in various keys.

(e) Developing a mastery of the entire range of the instrument. (Process) A combination of all the above.

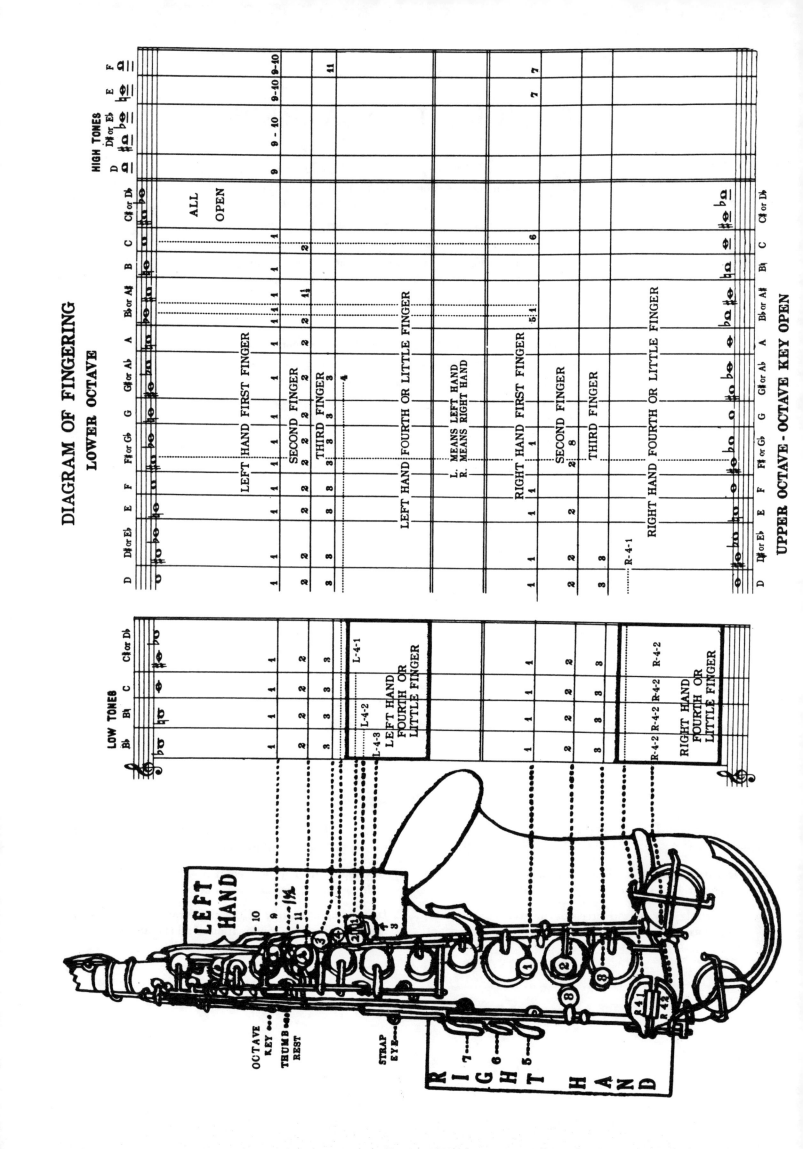

LESSON 1

OBJECTIVE: To review knowledge learned in Book I.

Scale of F Major

(One flat, B♭)

Scale of D Major

(Two sharps, F♯ and C♯)

Minka

Russian Song

A Hearty Dinner

Old English Song

The Little Sandman

Brahms

Long, Long Ago

(Duet)

LESSON 2

OBJECTIVE: 1. Application of the principle of using the octave key.

Reuben and Rachel

How Can I Leave Thee

Folk Song

Auld Lang Syne

Old Scottish Air

Massa's in the Cold, Cold Ground

Foster

LESSON 3

OBJECTIVES: 1. To learn the C Major scale and arpeggio (upper octave).
2. The playing of familiar melodies in the key of C Major.

Scale of C Major (upper octave)

(No sharps and no flats)

Arpeggio (broken chord)

All Through the Night

Welsh Folk-Song

Hymn

Mason

Blue Bells of Scotland

Old Scotch Air

LESSON 4

OBJECTIVES: 1. To learn the D Major scale (upper octave).
2. To play familiar melodies in the key of D Major.
3. To learn the meaning of dynamics (volume of tone)

Introducing high C sharp (♯)

Scale of D Major (upper octave)

Arpeggio

D Major Scale and Arpeggio in Two Octaves

O Come, All Ye Faithful

Moderato
Key of sharp is
mf (medium loud)
f (loud)
p (softly)
louder f

Home, Sweet Home

Duet
Bishop
Andante
Pupil
mf Practice both hands
THINK
Pupil

LESSON 5

OBJECTIVES: 1. Further practice using high C♯ and D.
2. Playing melodies in the key of D Major.

Theme
(from Violin Concerto)

Beethoven

LESSON 6

OBJECTIVES: 1. To learn the name and fingering for low C.
2. To learn the value and importance of firm finger action.
3. Playing the C Major scale and arpeggio. (lower octave.)

Introducing low C.
Played (L. 1-2-3) (R. 1-2-3)
plus R. (4-2)
See fingering chart—

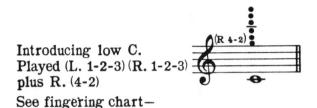

These lower notes are not easy to produce. Relax the lip pressure and blow a little stronger.

Scale and Arpeggio of C Major*
(Lower octave)
Half Steps (E to F) and (B to C)

Holy, Holy, Holy
Dykes

Home work: Mark the names of the notes in Ex. 3.
Learn to recite (spell) and play the C Major scale from memory.
*See lesson 3 for upper octave of this scale.

LESSON 7

OBJECTIVES. 1. To learn the name and fingering for low B.
2. Correlation of notes in the lower register, (name and position on staff) with proper fingering.
3. Playing familiar melodies involving the use of 8th notes in $\frac{4}{4}$ and $\frac{3}{4}$ time.

Introducing low B.
Played (L. 1-2-3) (R. 1-2-3)
plus (R. 4-2) and (L. 4-2)
See fingering chart.
Relaxed lip pressure.

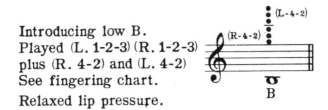

① Hold fingers firmly

② Name the notes in this exercise

③ Press fingers firmly

Deck the Hall

④ With motion (Con moto)

America*

⑤ Andante
Time sig. is

Home work:

---

*Try to play America in the key of G by ear. Hear the next tone and sense the fingering. It will start on G.
Home work: Learn to play teacher parts to duets in Lessons 2 and 3. Write line of notes studied below middle C Divide into measures and mark time signature. Use half, quarter and eighth notes.

LESSON 8

OBJECTIVE: Further practice using low C and B by playing familiar melodies.

Waltz

Trauts

Melody

Beethoven

Evening Song

von Weber

Dutch Dance

Folk Song

Melody in F

Rubinstein

CHROMATIC SCALES *

OBJECTIVES: 1. Understanding and playing chromatics
2. Knowledge of enharmonic tones.
3. Learning new fingerings.

Chromatics

The word "chromatic" means moving by half steps. A chromatic scale is one that ascends or descends by half steps.
ENHARMONIC tones are notes that sound the same though given a different name because they are on different degrees of the staff. Ex. F♯-G♭.

BE SURE TO LEARN THE PROPER FINGERING FOR BOTH ASCENDING AND DESCENDING CHROMATIC SCALES. YOUR TEACHER WILL SHOW YOU THE NEW FINGERINGS NECESSARY TO PLAY THESE SCALES.

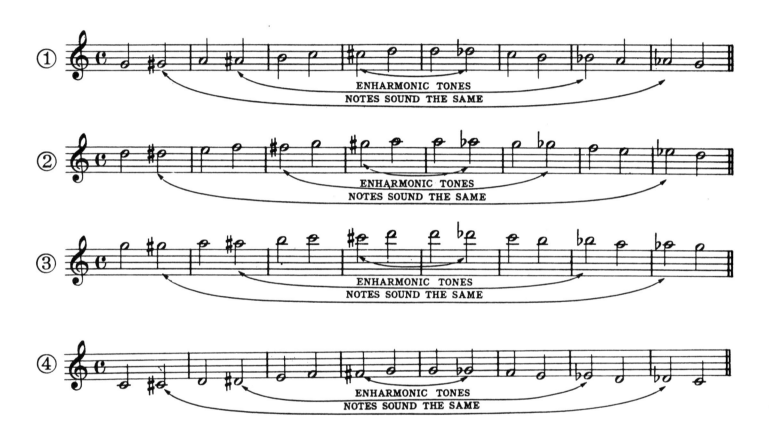

Chromatic Scale of C in Two Octaves

*The material on this page may be assigned whenever the teacher feels the need for chromatic scale study.

TEST QUESTIONS THROUGH LESSON 8

TEACHER: Write two lines of notes, one in the upper register, and one in the lower register as a check on fingering.

LESSON 9

OBJECTIVES: 1. Learning a new rhythm.
2. Understanding Alla breve. (cut time) (2/2 time)
3. Application of pre-knowledge in playing accidentals.

Alla breve or 2/2 time

Alla breve, (2/2) or cut time ¢ is played the same as 2/4 time. Each note has half the value as in 4/4 time, a half note being the unit of a beat.

Rhythm Drills

Play the following rhythm patterns, (A)-(B) etc. using the D Major scale (one or two octaves) as an exercise.

There's Music in the Air

Root

Think Count: & 1 & 2 & 1 2

LESSON 10

OBJECTIVES: 1. Continuation of Alla breve (cut time).
2. The playing of a full length march.
3. Application of pre-knowledge.

Advancement March*

* All marches generally consist of an introduction, 1st and 2nd strain, each repeated, followed by a Trio. The key of the trio is always a fifth lower than that of the first part.

**This sign 𝄎 means to repeat the preceding measure.

LESSON 11

OBJECTIVE: Further practice using Alla breve (cut time)

Marine's Hymn

Official Song
U.S. Marine Corps

Caisson Song

Maj. E. L. Gruber

Trio from Red and Blue March

Woodrow

Supplementary Material using (Cut time ¢)

NOTICE KEY SIGNATURES AND WHAT THEY MEAN

A Capital Ship

Old English Tune

In march time (Tempo marcia)

Theme from Der Freischütz

von Weber

Allegretto

College Song**

Allegro (Fast)

* *a tempo,* in the original tempo.
** This theme (melody) was used by Brahms in his Academic Festival Overture.

LESSON 12

OBJECTIVES: 1. To learn another new rhythm.
2. Knowledge and use of the rhythm of ⁶⁄₈ time.
3. Counting six to a measure and two to a measure.
4. Application of new rhythm in familiar melodies.

Six-Eight Time

Count six beats to each measure in slow tempo-an eighth note (♪) being the unit of a beat.

Count two beats to each measure in fast tempo-a dotted quarter note (♩.) being the unit of a beat.

Use the rhythmic patterns below in playing other scales you know to gain facility in fingering.

Home work: Write line of notes, using different rhythm patterns in ⁶⁄₈ time.

LESSON 13

OBJECTIVES : 1. Continuation of six-eight time (slow)
2. Application of pre-knowledge in familiar tunes
3. Playing a duet in six-eight time. Study both parts.

Barcarolle

Offenbach
(Adapted)

Moderato Observe slurs carefully

Think Count: 1 2 3 4 5 6

Folk Song

Allegretto

FINE

*D.C. al FINE**

Drink To Me Only With Thine Eyes

English Air

(Duet)

Andante

Pupil

Think, count carefully

Pupil

**D.C. (Da Capo) = Go back to the beginning and play to FINE.*

Music for Schools

A specially selected range of music books, tutors and reference books for schools and libraries.
From folk to pop, jazz to classics, every book is graded according to age and ability.

The Complete Guitar Player
by Russ Shipton

For classroom or private use. Easy to follow text with diagrams and demonstration photographs. Special bands of colour focus the attention of the guitarist on the music. All songs or solos are on one page or facing pages. Most of the course is based on the music of modern performers such as Bob Dylan, John Denver and The Beatles. Enables you to play right from lesson one to an advanced stage, and assumes you have no knowledge of music.
Book 1, also contains pull-out chord chart and unique tuning record. *(CD), AM 25123*
Book 2 *(CD), AM 25131*
Book 3 *(CD), AM 25149*
Book 4 *(CD), AM 25156*
Complete set of separate books also available. *AM 25164*

The Complete Guitar Player
Omnibus Edition Books 1, 2, 3, and 4 *(CD), AM 26691*

The Complete Guitar Player Cassettes

Four cassettes in all, one to each book of The Complete Guitar Player.
Cassette: Book 1 *(CD), OM 20004*
Cassette: Book 2 *(CD), OM 20012*
Cassette: Book 3 *(CD), OM 20038*
Cassette: Book 4 *(CD), OM 20046*

The Complete Guitar Player Chord Book
by Russ Shipton

Shows exactly what chords are needed to both play and arrange songs. Many clear photographs plus unique demonstration record.
(CD), AM 31717

Chord Book Cassette

This cassette supplements the contents of ''The Complete Guitar Player Chord Book''.
(CD), OM 20137

The Complete Guitar Player Video

Full colour teaching video lasting 60 minutes which is an important addition to The Complete Guitar Player series. A self-contained home study course.
VHS *(CD), OV 10002*
Beta *(CD), OV 10010*

The Complete Rock & Pop Guitar Player

Learn to play guitar in the style of Dire Straits, Duran Duran, Bruce Springsteen . . . right from lesson one. Easy-to-follow lessons, diagrams and demonstration photographs.
Book 1
Holding your guitar, tuning, chord changing. Pull out chord chart.
(CD), AM 60278
Book 2
Easy musical notation, tablature, rock and reggae strum patterns. Classic backing riffs, new chords.
(CD), AM 60286
Book 3
Introduction to harmony, new chords, arpeggio style accompaniment, modern rhythm styles, strumming effects.
(CD), AM 60294
Book 4
Electronic effects, new chords and backing styles, hammer-ons and pull-offs, new riffs, advanced techniques.
(CD), AM 60302

D.I.Y. Guitar Repair
by Pieter J. Fillet
Easy-to-follow instructions, plus 170 diagrams and photos. Slim format. *(CD), AM 38530*

Guitar Case Chord Book
by Peter Pickow
Fits into your guitar case. Clear readable diagrams and no page flipping. *(CD), AM 35841*

The Guitarist's Picture Chords
by Happy Traum
The most useful guitar chords in every key diagrammed in three different positions. The first position is accompanied by a photograph. *(CD), AM 16015*

The Guitarist's Picture Chord Encyclopedia
by John Pearse
Every chord you'll ever need to play shown in photographs, diagrams and standard notation. *(CD), OP 41797*

Instant Guitar: Play Today
Fastest way to learn guitar. Written in easy to follow language, it assumes no knowledge of music. Instructional record included. *(CD), AM 32517*

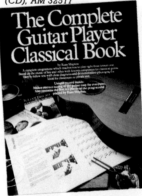

The Complete Guitar Player Classical Book
by Russ Shipton
The complete method clearly explained in text and many demonstration photographs. A collection of tunes to play. *(CD), AM 38217*

Solo Guitar Playing
by Frederick Noad
Instruction, including graded exercises, practice studies and a survey of the guitar repertoire etc. *(BD), OK 61994*

Solo Guitar Playing Book 2
by Frederick Noad
Technique, sight-reading, musicianship for the intermediate guitarist. Plus graded exercises and practice studies and an advanced repertoire of thirty works. *(BD), OP 40591*

Accompanying Tapes to Solo Guitar Playing
by Frederick Noad
Tape A: Exercises & Study Pieces, Page 43–Page 128. (BD), OM20236.
Tape B: Exercises & Study Pieces, Page 130–Page 213. (BD), OM20244
Double Cassette: Pack A & B. (BD), OM20293

Tuning Your Guitar
by Donald Brosnac
Fits into your guitar case. Easy-to-follow text and diagrams – will do wonders even for the so-called 'tone deaf'. *(CD), AM 35858*

Using Your Guitar
by Brook Hedick
Fits into your guitar case. Basic instruction, maintaining your guitar, tablature and song accompaniment etc. are some of the points covered in this comprehensive book. *(CD), AM 35783*

Songbooks with Guitar & Piano Accompaniments

The Beatles Complete: Guitar
(I), NO 17303

The Beatles Complete (Revised)
Guitar/Vocal: Melody line chord boxes and symbols, 388pp.
(I), NO 18145

The Complete Guitar Player Songbook
Contains all the songs and music featured in The Complete Guitar Player. In standard notation with diagrams and chord symbols plus full lyrics.
(EI), AM 26527

The Complete Guitar Player Songbook No.2
This new book contains 50 songs which are arranged in keys which are examined in 'The Complete Guitar Player' books. Includes chords, left hand fingerings and right hand rhythm pattern, also lyrics.
(EI), AM 31634.

The Complete Guitar Player Songbook No.3
Another 50 songs by Paul McCartney, The Rolling Stones, Buddy Holly etc. In standard notation with chord boxes and full lyrics. Useful references to The Complete Guitar Player Course are printed with each song.
(EI), AM 33291

The Complete Guitar Player Songbook No.4
Of special interest to players who have followed The Complete Guitar Player Course. 50 songs by Billy Joel, John Denver, Elvis Presley etc. Standard notation, chord boxes and full lyrics.
(EI), AM 33754

The Complete Guitar Player Songbook No.5
Fifty songs by David Bowie, Bob Marley, The Police and many others in standard notation with chord boxes and full lyrics.
(EI), AM 38027

The Complete Guitar Player Songbook No.6
Songs from Elvis Costello, Sting, Mark Knopfler and other stars. Fifty numbers in standard notation with chord boxes and lyrics.
(EI), AM 38209

Animal Songs For Children
More than 40 animal songs beloved by children the world over. Melody lines in standard notation with chord names. New piano accompaniment.
(E), AM 60062

The Beatles Complete: Piano/Vocal, Easy Organ
Almost every song composed and performed by The Beatles. Plus original photographs and full colour illustrations.
(E), NO 17162

The Beatles Complete (Revised)
Re-engraved, revised edition of 'Beatles Complete'. 203 songs – composed and recorded by the group.
Piano/Organ: Piano/vocal, chord symbols (E), NO 18160

The Joy Of Folk Songs
Contains eighty-two popular American songs and songs from other lands, all with lyrics and chord symbols.
(E), YK 21061

Nursery Rhymes And Songs
Over 40 nursery rhymes and songs. Illustrated throughout. Melody lines in standard notation together with chord names. Fun to learn and sing.
(E), AM 60211

It's Easy To Play Children's Songs
Seventeen songs for the modern child – to take their place alongside the traditional nursery rhymes. In easy piano arrangements with lyrics and chord symbols. Includes 'Banks of the Ohio', 'This Ole House' and 'Rivers of Babylon'.
(E), AM 29489

It's Easy To Play Christmas Songs
The world's best-loved carols and Christmas songs – twenty-one of them with words and chord symbols. Includes 'The First Nowell', 'Sleigh Ride' and 'Hark the Herald Angels Sing'.
(E), AM 22641

Hymns And Prayers For Children
Forty-two hymns and prayers. Complete with words, piano accompaniment and chord symbols. Easy to play.
(E), AM 38639

The Joy Of Disney
Easy piano arrangements of songs from Walt Disney's 'Bambi', 'Cinderella' and many others.
(E), WD 10278

Jumping, Laughing And Resting
Over ninety songs for children from 3-10 years old. Melody line in standard notation with chord names. Illustrated.
(E), AM 38621

The Lullaby Book
An illustrated collection of children's lullabies from all over the world. Easy-to-play arrangements with chord names and lyrics.
(A), AM 37029

New Songs For Children
Simplified arrangements of modern tunes such as 'A Windmill in Old Amsterdam', 'Grandad' and 'Yellow Submarine' – thirty in all. Words and chord symbols are included. Delightfully illustrated.
(E), AM 13798
Lyrics only (E), AM 30081

New Songs For Children, The Gingerbread Man Book
Simplified arrangements of the kind of music today's youngsters like to sing and play. 31 songs arranged for piano/vocal with guitar boxes.
(E), AM 36013

The Nursery Rhyme Book
Over one hundred well-loved songs and rhymes. Easy piano arrangement plus words and chord symbols to sixty-four.
(E), AM 26824

Piano Collections & Keyboard Tutors

Classics To Moderns

Each of the six graded volumes in the *Classics to Moderns* Series presents a range of piano music exactly as written by master composers from early Baroque to the present day. The works are ideal for study, sight reading or simply for enjoyment.

Book 1 *(E)*, YK 20014
Book 2 *(E)*, YK 20022
Book 3 *(I)*, YK 20030
Book 4 *(I)*, YK 20048
Book 5 *(I)*, YK 20055
Book 6 *(I)*, YK 20063
Complete Set *(I)*, YK 20071

More Classics To Moderns

Easy, original piano music as written by many famous composers.

Book 1 *(E)*, YK 20121
Book 2 *(E)*, YK 20139
Book 3 *(I)*, YK 20147
Book 4 *(I)*, YK 20154
Book 5 *(I)*, YK 20162
Book 6 *(I)*, YK 20170
Complete Set *(I)*, YK 20188

The Complete Keyboard Player
by Kenneth Baker

Teach yourself to play any make of electronic keyboard, make your keyboard sound like a single instrument or a whole orchestra. Book 1 includes pullout keyboard chart and record.

Book 1 *(E)*, AM 38308
Book 2 *(E)*, AM 38316
Book 3 *(E)*, AM 38324

The Complete Keyboard Player: Songbook 1

Popular numbers to play on the electronic keyboard. Includes 'Brown Girl In The Ring', 'Cecilia', 'Eight Days A Week' and 'Mary's Boy Child'.
(E), AM 39116

The Complete Keyboard Player: Songbook 2

Nineteen popular melodies including 'Amapola', 'Every Breath You Take', 'Here Comes The Sun' and 'Top Of The World'.
(E), AM 39124

The Complete Keyboard Player: Songbook 3

Music for the electronic keyboard, with lyrics to 19 numbers such as 'Georgia On My Mind', 'Eleanor Rigby', 'Those Were The Days' and 'Thank You For The Music'
(E), AM 39132

The Complete Piano Player
by Kenneth Baker

The only piano course based throughout on today's popular songs and famous light classics. Easy to follow text and clear demonstration diagrams. Book 1 with keyboard chart.

Book 1 *(E)*, AM 34828
Book 2 *(E)*, AM 34836
Book 3 *(E)*, AM 34844
Book 4 *(E)*, AM 34851
Book 5 *(E)*, AM 34869

The Complete Piano Player Collection

A unique collection of music. Each book is divided into solos, folk songs, etudes, sonatinas and duets.

Book 1 *(EI)*, PB 40831
Book 2 *(EI)*, PB 40849
Book 3 *(EI)*, PB 40856
Book 4 *(EI)*, PB 40864

Denes Agay's Learning To Play Piano

A progression of melodic pieces and studies teaching the basics step by step. This new course offers a fresh, unhurried, and sound approach to piano study as well as providing a melodic repertoire for the young player.
Book 1: Primer *(A)*, YK20845

Denes Agay's Learning To Play Piano
Book 2: *(A)*, YK20493

Denes Agay's Learning To Play Piano
Book 3 *(A)*, YK20501

Denes Agay's Learning To Play Piano
Book 4 *(A)*, YK20519

Start Playing Creative Keyboard
by Gabriel Butler and Mick Barker

Apply a few simple rules and techniques and discover a new world of creative playing on your keyboard. Useful tips and advice plus 16 famous popular songs.
(D), AM66663

Start Playing Keyboard
by Peter Lavender

An easy-to-follow course which starts you playing electronic keyboard right away, even if you have no knowledge of music. Includes 28 popular songs.
(E), AM 36906

Start Playing Keyboard Book 2
by Peter Lavender

Play 'fingered' chords with the left hand, improve your sight reading and playing technique and progress from SFX letter-note music to standard music notation. 16 popular numbers including 'We've Only Just Begun' and 'Yellow Submarine'.
(D), AM65749

Cats
The fabulous hit musical by Andrew Lloyd Webber. Based on 'Old Possum's Book of Practical Cats' by T.S. Eliot. All the songs arranged for piano with lyrics and chord symbols.
(BCD), AM 31006

Walt Disney Vocal Selections: Cinderella
Arranged for piano, with lyrics and chord symbols.
(B), WD 10039

The Jungle Book
Vocal selection arranged for piano/vocal, with guitar chord symbols.
(ABC), WD 10013

Evita
Musical excerpts and libretto.
(CD), EVM 10005

The New Illustrated Disney Songbook
Seventy-three memorable Disney songs from such favourite films as 'Snow White and the Seven Dwarfs', 'Pinocchio', 'Cinderella', 'The Jungle Book' and many more. Arranged for piano/vocal with guitar boxes. Full colour illustrations.
(CD), OP44031

Walt Disney's Bambi Songbook
All the songs from the film. Arranged for piano/vocal with chord boxes. Colour illustrations.
(AB), CC11321

Smike
Libretto *(B), AV 51860*
Vocal Score *(B), AV 51878*

The Walt Disney Songbook
Walt Disney favourites from 'Davy Crockett', 'The Jungle Book', 'Bedknobs And Broomsticks', 'Cinderella', 'Mary Poppins', 'The Happiest Millionaire', 'Pinocchio', 'Snow White' and other shows. 25 numbers for piano with lyrics and chord symbols.
(C), AM19316

The Complete Guitar Player Music Writing Book
The only music writing book specially compiled for guitarists. Enables you to keep a complete record of your own songs and repertoire.
64pp, AM 34208

The Complete Guitar Player Music Writing Pad
Sixty-four pages, each containing ten blank chord diagrams and 6 staves for notation.
64pp, AM 34216

Woodstock Music Manuscript Paper
A4, 12 stave, *32pp, WO 10166*
A4, 12 stave, spiral, *32pp, WO 10174*
A5L, 6 stave, spiral *32pp, WO 10224*
A5L, 6 stave stitched, *32pp, WO 10216*
A4, 12 stave, punched, *48pp, WO 10182*
A4, 12 stave, *64pp, WO 10190*
A4, 12 stave, spiral, *64pp, WO 10208*

The Complete Guitar Player Video
with Russ Shipton
Full colour teaching video lasting 60 minutes which is an important addition to The Complete Guitar Player series. A self-contained home study course.
VHS *(CD), OV 10002*
Beta *(CD), OV 10010*

How To Read Music
with Frederick Noad
Even if you have never read a note of music, this 51-minute, full-colour video will teach you how. Ideal for classroom or private teaching.
VHS *(CD), OV 10028*
Beta *(CD), OV 10093*

Jigsaw
Popular tunes for school orchestras. This series of flexible arrangements may be used with players of wide ranging abilities. Pack includes Conductor Score and parts for instruments including piano, recorder, violin, euphonium, cello, flute, bass, oboe and trumpet etc.
EastEnders *(BC), AM65798*
I Know Him So Well *(BC), AM66747*

We Wish You A Merry Christmas
by Barrie Carson Turner
Five variations scored for classroom ensemble and piano. This pack includes: piano/conductor score, 6 recorder and 4 each tuned and untuned percussion parts.
(BC), AM65202

Fiddler On The Roof
Vocal selections from the show. 11 numbers including 'If I Were A Rich Man' and 'Sunrise, Sunset'.
(D), AM 39520

Jesus Christ Superstar
Musical excerpts and complete libretto.
(CD), LE 11110

Clarinet

Beatles, Themes And Variations: Clarinet
Seven Beatles themes with three variations. Pull-out piano accompaniment. Also for flute and trumpet.
(I), NO 17873

Graded Solos For Clarinet
Forty popular songs selected and arranged by Robin de Smet. Also for flute and trumpet.
(EI), AM 33598

Lennon & McCartney For Clarinet
This book presents over fifty compositions arranged for the clarinet. Also for trumpet and flute.
(I), NO 17725

100 Solos: Clarinet
Graded solos for players of all standards. Each piece is complete in itself and requires no piano accompaniment. Also for flute, saxophone, trumpet and violin.
(EI), AM 33689

101 Popular Songs For Trumpet And Clarinet
Arranged in solo and duet form. A collection of popular and traditional tunes.
(EI), HS 10445

The Complete Clarinet Player
by Paul Harvey
Based on popular songs and light classics. Clear text, diagrams, photographs.
Book 1
Blow your first notes and learn the rudiments of music. Play songs such as 'Love Me Tender', 'Yellow Submarine' . . . Fingering chart.
(CD), AM62613
Book 2 (CD), AM62621
Book 3 (CD), AM62639
Book 4 (CD), AM62647

Associated Board Examination Grades
(E) Elementary – Grades 1-3
(I) Intermediate – Grades 4-6
(Ad) Advanced – Grades 6-8
(T) Teacher's Book

Flute

Beatles, Themes And Variations: Flute
Seven Beatles themes with three variations. Pull-out piano accompaniment. Also for clarinet and trumpet.
(I), NO 17865

50 Selected Children's Classics
Includes 'Arabesque', 'Barcarolle' and 'Canon in D'. Also for recorder and piano.
(E), HS 10551

Flute Solos (EFS 38)
Effective arrangements of over 50 pieces. The wide range of compositions includes works of Beethoven, Brahms, Dvořák, Schubert and many others as well as folk songs, dances' jigs and reels from all over the world. Each piece includes piano accompaniment.
(BCD), AM 40197

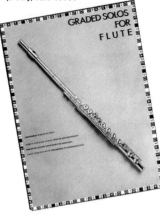

Graded Solos For Flute
Forty popular songs selected and arranged by Robin de Smet. Also for clarinet and trumpet.
(BD), AM 33812

Lennon & McCartney For Flute
This book presents over fifty compositions arranged for the flute. Also for trumpet and clarinet.
(I), NO 17717

100 Solos: Flute
Graded solos for players of all standards. Each piece is complete and does not require piano accompaniment. Also for clarinet, saxophone, trumpet and violin.
(EI), AM 33812

One Hundred And One Solos For The Flute
An outstanding collection of popular and light classical music arranged by Robin De Smet. Includes 'Chanson Triste', 'EastEnders' and 'The Power Of Love'.
(CD), AM63538

Selected Flute Solos (EFS 101)
This volume contains a group of the finest standard flute solos selected for their diversity in style and suitability for concert and contest use. Among the selections are works by Pessard, Chaminade, Mozart, Handel, Mendelssohn, Gluck, Fauré and Godard. All have piano accompaniment.
(Ad), AM 40403

The Complete Flute Player
by John Sands
The only flute course using popular tunes. Clear text, photographs and diagrams.
Book 1
Assembling the flute and producing your first sounds. Left hand notes, music notation and 7 keys. Music by Lennon & McCartney and John Denver etc.
(CD), AM62852
Book 2 (CD), AM62860
Book 3 (CD), AM62878
Book 4 (CD), AM62886

Penny Whistle

How To Play The Penny Whistle
by Gina Landor & Phil Cleaver
No previous knowledge required. Illustrated with clear diagrams. Also contains many popular tunes to play.
(E), AM 27137

The Penny Whistle Book
by Robin Williamson
A complete guide to the penny whistle for beginning to advanced players using a new systematic approach to fingering. Contains information on modal playing and 56 penny whistle tunes. Superb as a beginner's text, also of great use to the advanced player.
(EIAd), OK 63271

Recorder

Abba Songs For The Recorder
A selection of favourite Abba songs specially arranged for the recorder. Published complete with lyrics and guitar diagrams plus a two-page introduction to playing the recorder. Includes 'Waterloo' and 'Knowing Me, Knowing You'.
(I), AM 19720

Appalachian Folk Songs For Recorder
by Ralph Wm. Zeitlin
Thirty traditional folk songs and tunes arranged as solos and duets for soprano and alto recorders.
(I), AM 35650

Around The World With My Recorder
by Harry Dexter
Includes 101 selected song favourites in easy to play recorder arrangements.
(E), HS 11542

Bach For Recorder
by Cliff Tobey
Solos and duets arranged for soprano and tenor recorders.
(IAd), AY 15406

Baroque & Folk Tunes For The Recorder
An unusual collection of music arranged for the recorder – fifty pieces from over 300 years of music.
(I), AM 17948

Beatles For Recorder
Easy new arrangements by Robin de Smet, of famous Beatles songs. Thirty tunes with chord symbols.
(E), AM 18434

Beatles Songs For The Recorder
Outstanding collection of Beatles songs arranged specially for recorder. Complete with lyrics and guitar diagrams. Includes a two-page introduction to playing the recorder.
(I), NO 17394

Children's Songs For The Recorder
Twenty-five songs especially arranged for recorder with lyrics and guitar chord boxes.
(I), AM 13673

Christmas Songs For The Recorder
Over 20 of the best known Christmas carols arranged for recorder with lyrics and guitar boxes.
(E), AM 20157

Walt Disney Songs For The Recorder
Twenty-five outstanding selections from the shows and films which will always be associated with Walt Disney. Includes lyrics and guitar boxes.
(I), WD 10070

Early Music For Recorder
arranged by Robin de Smet
Easy new arrangements of airs and dances from the 10th to the 16th century. 47 tunes with chord symbols.
(E), AM 36542

Elizabethan Music For Recorder
by Ralph Wm. Zeitlin
Solos, duets, trios and rounds arranged for soprano, alto and tenor recorders.
(I), AY 15315

50 Selected Children's Classics
Includes 'Arabesque', 'Barcarolle', 'Canon in D'. Also for flute and piano.
(E), HS 10569

50 Songs For Recorder Book 1
For recorder with guitar accompaniment. Includes 'California Dreaming', 'Fernando' and 'Bright Eyes'.
(I), AM 29885

50 Songs For Recorder Book 2
For recorder and guitar accompaniment. Includes 'Top of the World', 'Little Buttercup' and 'Sailing'.
(I), AM 29893

Film Music For The Recorder
Twenty-eight well known film titles arranged for recorder, with lyrics and guitar boxes.
(I), AM 25701

Film And TV Themes For The Recorder
Over 20 notable tunes used as film and TV themes with lyrics and guitar chord boxes.
(I), AM 13962

Folk Songs For The Recorder
Twenty-seven famous folk songs arranged for recorder, with lyrics and guitar boxes.
(I), AM 29000

How To Play The Recorder
Pocket size recorder tutor which is a complete course for the beginner that is easy and fun to play.
(E), AM 35551

Hymns For Recorder
Easy new arrangements by Robin de Smet of 34 best loved hymn tunes. With chord symbols and words.
(E), AM 36559

Irish Music For Recorder
New easy arrangements by Robin de Smet of famous Irish songs and melodies. 30 tunes with chord symbols.
(E), AM 36534

Jazz For The Recorder
A contrasting selection of popular and jazz standards. Includes lyrics and guitar chord boxes.
(I), AM 28994

Paul McCartney: Songs for the Recorder
Twenty-seven songs including 'Mull of Kintyre', 'My Love'. With lyrics and guitar diagrams plus a 2-page introduction to playing the recorder.
(I), MY 70358

My Very First Recorder Songbook. Book A
Fifteen easy to play songs, folk tunes and songs from shows and films. With piano accompaniment and separate recorder part.
(E), AM 34158
Book B
(E), AM 34166

New Popular Songs For The Recorder
Published complete with lyrics and guitar chord boxes.
(E), AM 31501

Oliver: Songs For The Recorder
Outstanding selection from the show, with lyrics and guitar chord boxes, plus a six-page introduction to playing the recorder.
(I), AM 13368

Paul Simon Songs For The Recorder
Twenty songs including lyrics and guitar diagrams plus a two-page introduction to playing the recorder.
(I), PS 10016

Songs And Dances Of England
An outstanding collection of songs and dances from England's musical heritage. Arranged for voice and recorder, penny whistle or flute, or other suitable 'C' instruments.
(EI), AM 31428

Songs And Dances Of Ireland
A collection of songs from Ireland's rich musical heritage. All arranged for voice and recorder, penny whistle or flute, or other suitable 'C' instrument.
(EI), AM 31402

Songs And Dances Of Scotland
An exciting collection of songs and dances all arranged for voice and recorder, flute, penny whistle or other 'C' instrument. With chord symbols and guitar diagrams, plus full lyrics.
(EI), AM 31410

Cat Stevens Songs For The Recorder
Complete with lyrics and guitar boxes. Plus a two page introduction to playing the recorder.
(I), AM 23425

10 Famous Pop Songs For Recorder
For solos or ensemble playing. Piano accompaniment available. Can be played with any other instrument in the series. Includes 'Michelle' and 'Unforgettable'. Lyrics and chord symbols. Also for violin, saxophone, flute, clarinet and trumpet.
(E), AM 28614
Piano Accompaniments
(E), AM 28507

Together For Two Recorders And Guitar
A variety of music ranging from Purcell to Pop. Mozart's 'Allegro' is joined by melodies such as 'Clementine' and 'Rivers Of Babylon'. With lyrics, chord symbols and guitar boxes.
Book 1 *(E), AM 29901*

Together For Two Recorders And Guitar
For C Recorders and guitars playing in ensemble. Boccherini's 'Minuet' to 'Yesterday'. Lyrics, chord symbols, and guitar boxes.
Book 2 *(E), AM 29919*

Associated Board Examination Grades
(E) Elementary – Grades 1-3
(I) Intermediate – Grades 4-6
(Ad) Advanced – Grades 6-8
(T) Teacher's Book

Continued . . .

Saxophone

101 Easy Sax Solos & Duets
A collection of popular and traditional tunes.
(E), HS 11864

100 Solos: Saxophone
Graded solos for players of all standards. Each piece is complete in itself and requires no piano accompaniment. Also for clarinet, flute, recorder, trumpet and violin.
(EI), AM 33697

The Complete Saxophone Player
by Raphael Ravenscroft
This course is based on popular tunes and light classics. With clear text, diagrams and photographs it will prove easy to understand even to those with no knowledge of music.
Book 1 (CD), AM62712
Book 2 (CD), AM62720
Book 3 (CD), AM62738
Book 4 (CD), AM62746

All books in this catalogue are available from your local music dealer.
In case of difficulty contact:
Music Sales Limited
Newmarket Road, Bury St Edmunds IP33 3YB.

Trumpet

The Complete Trumpet Player
by Don Bateman
Based on popular songs and light classics. Clear text, diagrams, photographs.
Book 1
Rudiments of music, technique, the notes Low G to High D. Play songs such as 'I'd Like To Teach The World To Sing' and 'Edelweiss'.
(CD), AM39207
Book 2 (CD), AM39215
Book 3 (CD), AM39223
Book 4 (CD), AM39231

101 Solos For The Trumpet
arranged by Robin De Smet
An outstanding collection of music for trumpet covering a wide range of popular and light classical music.
(CD), AM61870

Popular Solos For The Trumpet
Over 30 hits from today's top artists. Includes 'Caribbean Queen', 'Walk Of Life', 'We Don't Need Another Hero' and 'When The Going Gets Tough'. No piano accompaniment required.
(CD), AM63108

Violin

100 Solos For Violin
Graded solos for players of all standards. The pieces are complete in themselves and require no piano accompaniment. Includes 'Dancing Queen', 'Michelle' and 'English Country Garden'.
(CD), AM33671

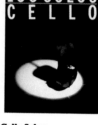

100 Cello Solos
Graded solos for players of all standards. The pieces are complete in themselves and require no accompaniment.
(CD), AM63231

Cello Solos
Easy to intermediate arrangements designed to bring out the finest qualities of the cello.
(CD), AM64486

Christmas Solos

Christmas Solos For The Clarinet
arranged by Robin De Smet
A unique collection of 49 traditional and up-to-date Christmas songs including 'Santa Claus Is Comin' To Town', 'When Santa Got Stuck Up The Chimney', 'Winter Wonderland' and many more. With chord symbols.
(CD), AM65020

Christmas Solos For The Flute
arranged by Robin De Smet
A unique collection of 53 traditional and up-to-date Christmas songs including 'Frosty The Snowman', 'I Believe In Father Christmas', 'Santa Claus Is Comin' To Town'. With chord symbols.
(CD), AM65038

Christmas Solos For The Recorder
arranged by Robin De Smet
A unique collection of 50 traditional and up-to-date Christmas songs including 'Away In A Manger', 'Silent Night', 'Santa Claus Is Comin' To Town' and 'Winter Wonderland'.
(CD), AM65046

Christmas Solos For The Bb Saxophone
arranged by Robin De Smet
A unique collection of more than 50 traditional and up-to-date Christmas songs including 'The First Nowell', 'Santa Claus Is Comin' To Town', 'Silent Night' and 'Winter Wonderland'. With chord symbols.
(CD), AM65061

Christmas Solos For The Trumpet
arranged by Robin De Smet
A unique collection of 49 traditional and up-to-date Christmas songs including 'Santa Claus Is Comin' To Town', 'When Santa Got Stuck Up The Chimney', 'Winter Wonderland' and many more. With chord symbols.
(CD), AM65053

Christmas Solos For The Violin
Standard carols and songs for the festive season arranged for the beginning-to-intermediate player. Chord symbols facilitate optional piano or guitar accompaniment.
(CD), AM67133

LESSON 14

OBJECTIVES: 1. Continuation of six-eight time. (slow)
2. Counting six beats to a measure.
3. To learn the meaning of ritard. (rit.)
4. Use of dynamics. (cresc. dim.)

It Came Upon a Midnight Clear

Willis

My Bonny

Scottish Song

LESSON 15

OBJECTIVES: 1. To learn to count six-eight time in fast tempo.
2. Counting two beats to a measure as in march time.

BEFORE PLAYING THIS LESSON REVIEW LESSON 12, THIS TIME AS FAST SIX-EIGHT TIME COUNTING TWO BEATS TO A MEASURE.

The Lion Hunt

Saverio

Trio from Our Director's March

Bigelow

Jumping Jack

H.M.S.

*Go back to the sign and play to *FINE*

LESSON 16

OBJECTIVES: 1. Continuation of six-eight time. (fast)
2. Counting two beats to a measure. (march time)
3. Application of pre-knowledge in the playing of a duet.
4. Playing of a march in six-eight time.

Funiculi-Funicula
(Duet)

TEST QUESTIONS THROUGH LESSON 16

		Points	Your score

1. Notate (write) the upper octave of the **D** major scale. — 10 ·········

·········

2. What is the meaning of (f)?_____ (p)?_____ (mf)? _____ — 5 ·········

3. What are enharmonic tones?_____ — 5 ·········

4. Write the enharmonic tones of the following notes. — 5 ·········

·········

5. What is meant by chromatic?_____ — 5 ·········

6. This sign **¢** means _____ . — 5 ·········

7. A half note in (**¢**) time receives _____ count. — 5 ·········

8. What is meant by six-eight (**⁶⁄₈**) time?_____ — 5 ·········

9. This note [music notation] in slow **⁶⁄₈** time has _____ counts. — 5 ·········

10. The above note in fast **⁶⁄₈** time has _____ counts. — 5 ·········

11. This note [music notation] in slow **⁶⁄₈** time has _____ counts. In fast time it has _____. — 5 ·········

12. Mark the count under the following. Slow tempo. — 5 ·········

·········

13. Divide the following into measures (note time signature). — 5 ·········

·········

14. This sign **⁒** means _____ . — 5 ·········

15. In **⁶⁄₈** march time (fast) the count is _____ beats to each measure. — 5 ·········

16. Inspection of instrument. — 10 ·········

17. Sight reading. — 10 ·········

— 100

TEACHER: Write line of notes in slow six-eight time in the key of C.

LESSON 17

OBJECTIVES: 1. To learn the name and fingering for fourth space E♭.
2. To learn the name and fingering for first line E♭.
3. To learn the meaning of the key of B♭ major.
4. To play familiar melodies in the key of B♭ major.

Introducing 4th space E♭
T (L-123) (R-123) (R-4-1)

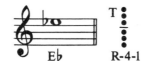

Introducing 1st line E♭
(L-123) (R-123) (R-4-1)

Key of B♭ Major
(Two flats: B♭ and E♭)

Hymn
Ritter

Waltz
Behr

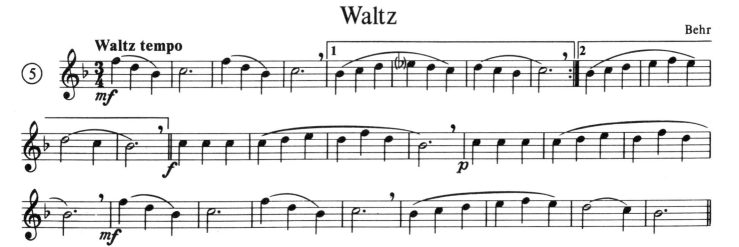

Theme from Surprise Symphony
Haydn

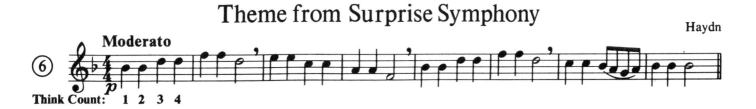

LESSON 18

OBJECTIVES: 1. To learn an alternate fingering for B♭.
2. To learn when to use this new fingering.
3. Practical application of this fingering by playing melodies.

Introducing an alternate fingering for 3rd line B♭
Played (L-1) (R-1)

Introducing an alternate fingering for 2nd space above the staff B♭
Played (T-L-1) (R-1)

THIS FINGERING IS USED ONLY WHEN THE NOTE (F) COMES BEFORE OR AFTER B♭. IT WILL BE INDICATED AS (A1).

Taps

Bugle Call

Ten Little Indians

Folk Song

Think Count: 1   2 & 3   4 &

The Merry Widow

Lehar

Think Count: 1 2   3

The Climate

LESSON 19

OBJECTIVES: 1. To learn another alternate fingering for B♭.
2. To learn when to use this new fingering.
3. Practical application of this fingering by playing melodies.

Introducing another alternate fingering for 3rd line B♭
Played (L-1 plus 1½)

Introducing another alternate fingering for 2nd space above the staff B♭
Played T (L-1 plus 1½)

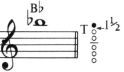

THIS FINGERING IS USED ONLY WHEN THE NOTE (G) COMES BEFORE OR AFTER B♭.
KEY (1 & 1½) ARE PLAYED SIMULTANEOUSLY WITH THE SAME FINGER. (FIRST FINGER OF
THE LEFT HAND). THIS FINGERING WILL BE INDICATED AS (2).

Taps

Bugle Call

Skip To My Lou

Folk Song

Think Count: 1 2 & 3 4 &

Volga Boatman

Russian Song

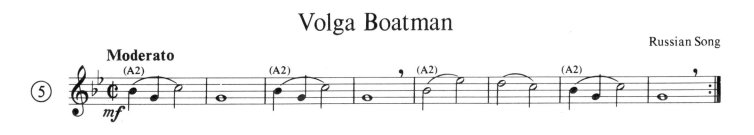

Melody

C.P.H.

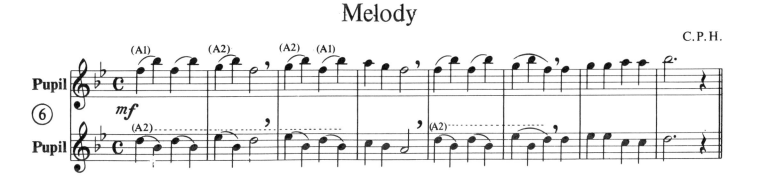

Supplementary Material in the keys of F, B♭ & D Major*

Jeanie With the Light Brown Hair

Foster

Old Folks at Home
Duet

Foster

Cradle Song

Brahms

Name the sharps

Practice both octaves

Teacher: These pieces should be used when the corresponding scale is assigned for study.

LESSON 20

OBJECTIVES: 1. To learn the meaning and use of sixteenth notes.
     (a) Equivalents.
     (b) Counting sixteenth notes.
    2. The playing of etudes and pieces using sixteenth notes.

Sixteenth Notes

A sixteenth note ♬ is equal to half the value of an eighth note. ♪ Two sixteenth notes equal one eighth-note ♬ = ♪ and four sixteenth notes equal one quarter note ♬♬ = ♩ Abbreviations for sixteenth notes are ♪. ♬ ♪. ♬♬

Bird Song

Kingdom Comin'

Mendelssohn

Scale Study**

* In this piece, which requires a slow movement, (andante) it is better to divide the $\frac{2}{4}$ time into $\frac{4}{8}$ (one count to each eighth note)

** Practice the above scale study with staccato tonguing.

LESSON 21

OBJECTIVES: 1. Further practice using sixteenth notes.
2. Application of pre-knowledge in playing melodies.

Skip To My Lou

Folk Song

Ten Little Indians

Folk Song

Canadian Folk Song

Moment Musical

Schubert

American Patrol

Meacham

LESSON 22

OBJECTIVES: 1. To learn dotted eighth and sixteenth notes, legato.
2. To learn the correct division of each beat.
3. Application of new rhythm.

Dotted Eighth and Sixteenth Notes
Legato (Connected)

This is one of the more difficult rhythms to learn. The dotted eighth note is equal to three sixteenth notes. Always feel a division of four on each beat when playing this rhythm, three on the dotted eighth and one on the sixteenth

BE SURE TO PLAY THE DOTTED EIGHTH NOTE LONG ENOUGH AND THE SIXTEENTH NOTE SHORT ENOUGH.

Largo
New World Symphony
(Duet)
Dvořák

Home work: Write line of notes, using dotted eighth and sixteenth notes.
cresc. Gradually louder.

LESSON 23

OBJECTIVES: 1. To learn dotted eighth and sixteenth notes, staccato.
2. Application of this difficult rhythm in familiar melodies using $\frac{2}{4}$ and $\frac{4}{4}$ time.

Dotted Eighth and Sixteenth Notes
Staccato (Detached)

Dotted eighth and sixteenth notes played staccato (detached) are separated by a short pause. Take notice how these notes are written and how they are actually played.

Home work: Memorize one of the melodies on this page.

LESSON 24

OBJECTIVE: Continued application of dotted eighth and
sixteenth notes in $\frac{3}{4}$ and $\frac{6}{8}$ time.

Maryland, My Maryland
(Duet)

Silent Night, Holy Night
(Duet)

Grüber

LESSON 25
Triplets

Triplets are groups of three notes played in the time of two note of the same value. They are indicated by a figure 3 and a slur placed over or under a group of three notes. A triplet of eighth notes is equal to two eighth notes or one quarter note

A measure of 2/4 containing two triplets is the same as a measure of 6/8 in march time

War March of the Priests
Mendelssohn

Pilgrims Chorus
Wagner

Theme from Maritana
Wallace

LESSON 26

OBJECTIVE: Further practice using triplets.

Theme from 5th Symphony

Tschaikowsky

Study in Triplets

America

(Variation in Triplets)

Carey

LESSON 27

OBJECTIVES: 1. To learn the name and fingering for high & low G-sharp.
2. To learn the name and fingering for high & low A-flat.
3. To learn to play the A major scale & arpeggio.
4. Playing melodies in the key of A major.
5. To understand the meaning of enharmonic tones. See page 9.

G♯ and A♭ are enharmonic tones *

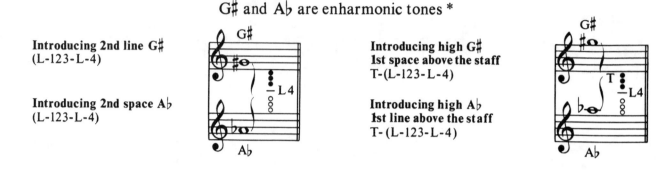

Introducing 2nd line G♯
(L-123-L-4)

Introducing 2nd space A♭
(L-123-L-4)

Introducing high G♯
1st space above the staff
T-(L-123-L-4)

Introducing high A♭
1st line above the staff
T-(L-123-L-4)

Scale of A Major

(Key signature; Three sharps, F♯-C♯-G♯)

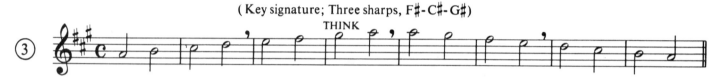

Good King Wenceslas

Carol

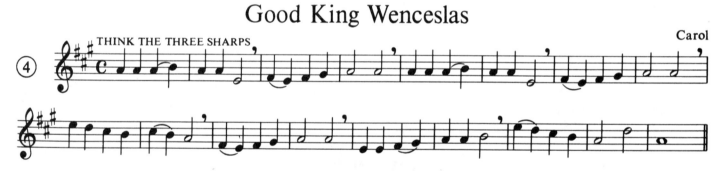

While Strolling Through the Park

Haley
(A)

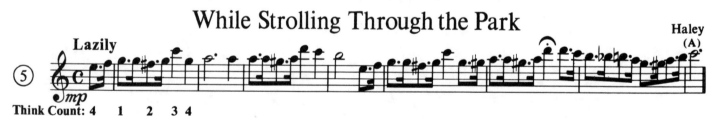

Think Count: 4   1   2   3 4

Listen to the Mocking Bird

Hawthorne

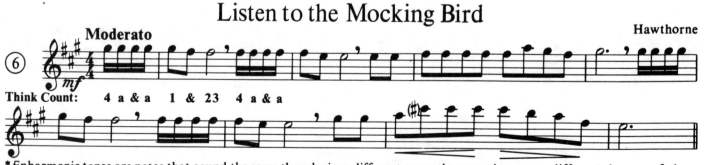

Think Count: 4 a & a   1 & 23   4 a & a

*Enharmonic tones are notes that sound the same though given different names because they are on different degrees of the staff. Ex. G♯ - A♭

The use of Accidentals and Chromatics
in the Playing of Familiar Melodies

LEARN TO TAKE PARTICULAR NOTICE OF THE KEY SIGNATURE BEFORE PLAYING

The Star Spangled Banner

John Stafford Smith

America, the Beautiful

Ward

*A sharp or B flat.

TEST QUESTIONS THROUGH LESSON 27

		Points	Your score
1.	These 𝄞 𝄴 ♪♪♪♪ 𝄽 𝄼 are _____ notes.	5	....
2.	Four (4) of the above notes equal a _____ note.	5	....
3.	Divide the following into measures.	5	....

$$\frac{4}{4} \ \text{♩ ♬♬ ♩ \ ♩ ♩ \ ♬♬ ♫ \ ♫♫ ♫ ♩ ♩ \ ♫♫ ♩ ♩ ♩ \ ♫♫} \ \|$$

		Points	Your score
4.	Circle the notes in the following that begin each beat.	8	....

$$\frac{4}{4} \ \text{♬♬ ♫ ♩ ♩ ♩ | ♫♫ ♩ ♩ ♫ | ♫♫ ♫ ♫♫ ♩ ♩ | ♫♫ ♫ ♩ ♫} \ \|$$

		Points	Your score
5.	A ♩ note is equal to _____ sixteenth notes.	5	....
6.	A ♪. note is equal to _____ sixteenth notes.	5	....
7.	This ♩.♬.♩ is equal to a _____ note.	5	....
8.	Write five measures in 4/4 time, using dotted-eighth and sixteenth notes.	10	....

𝄞 4/4 _____

		Points	Your score
9.	Divide the following into measures.	7	....

$$\frac{4}{4} \ \text{♩.♫.♩ ♩ ♫♫ ♩ ♩ | ♫. ♩. ♪ ♩ ♫. ♩ ♫. ♩ ♬♬ ♫.♫.♩} \ \|$$

		Points	Your score
10.	Write a line of notes in 3/4 time using dotted-eighth and sixteenth notes.	10	....

𝄞 3/4 _____

		Points	Your score
11.	Write a line of notes in 6/8 time using dotted-eighth and sixteenth notes.	10	....

𝄞 6/8 _____

		Points	Your score
12.	These ♩♩♩ (3) are called _____ .	5	....
13.	Inspection of instrument.	10	....
14.	Sight reading.	<u>10</u>	....
		100	

𝄞 _____

TEACHER: Write line of notes using dotted eighth and sixteenth notes, slurs, accidentals etc.

FINAL GRADE FOR THE YEAR............

Scales and Arpeggios (Chords)

The material on this page may be assigned whenever the teacher feels the need for scale and chord studies.
Play the following scales and chords as indicated; also play as follows:

ALWAYS NOTICE THE KEY SIGNATURE; IT IS A GUIDE FOR PROPER FINGERING

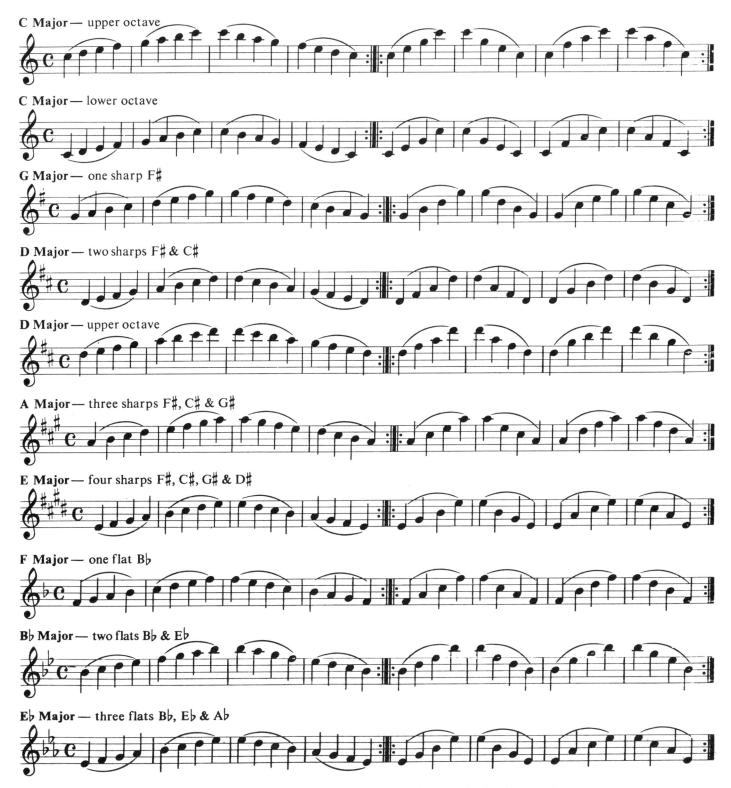

Home work: Place a sharp or flat before the notes affected by the key signature in the above scale.

Onward, Christian Soldiers

(Trio)

Sir Arthur Sullivan